I AM a REBEL GiRL

BY

a JOURNAL TO START REVOLUTIONS

FRANCESCA CAVALLO
ELENA FAVILLI

I AM a REBEL GIRL

I AM a REBEL GiRL

a JOURNAL TO START REVOLUTIONS

FRANCESCA CAVALLO
ELENA FAVILLI

REBEL GiRLS®

Good Night Stories for Rebel Girls and all other Rebel Girls titles are available for bulk purchase for sale promotions, premiums, fundraising, and educational needs.
For details, write to sales@rebelgirls.com.

www.rebelgirls.com

Costco Paperback Edition: July 2020
10 9 8 7 6 5 4 3 2 1

Created by Francesca Cavallo and Elena Favilli
Art Direction by Giulia Flamini
Graphic Design by Annalisa Ventura
Illustrations by Martina Paukova, Kate Prior, and Camila Rosa
Cover Design by Kate Prior

ISBN: 978-1-7348770-3-8

Printed in China

MIX
From responsible sources
FSC
www.fsc.org   FSC® C124807

**Freedom
is the destination,
And the map
is yours to draw.**

★ Contents ★

✴ Introduction ✴

Dearest Rebel,

Growing up as little girls, we've been taught to color within the lines that other people have drawn for us. We've been taught to say "yes" even when we wanted to say "no." We've been taught to take up as little space as we could.

It's time to stop passing these lessons on.

With this journal, we give you a mirror to explore your identity without fear. We can reach equality only if we stop frantically selecting the few parts of ourselves that are acceptable to society and embrace the fact that we have the right to be whole.

This is the place where you can celebrate your ambition without reserve, love your body without shame, organize rallies, plan businesses, and work out the details of your adventurous life.

So, if the world tells you to shrink, we'll ask you to visualize yourself as a giant. If the world tells you to be quiet, we'll pass you a megaphone! If the world questions women's rights, we'll give you space to write your own bill of rights.

I Am a Rebel Girl is designed to help you train your rebel spirit, embrace your potential with joy and determination, and be an agent of change.

The Good Night Stories for Rebel Girls series is about the daring deeds of many great women. *I Am a Rebel Girl* is about you, your story, and your revolution.

When you hold this journal, know that you are not alone. Sitting at many other desks and kitchen tables, or hunched over their legs on a train or on a bus, there are many other girls and women who, just like you, are dreaming, drawing, and building a different world.

We can't wait to see what you will accomplish!

Yours,
Francesca Cavallo
Elena Favilli

I AM a REBEL GIRL

This is how I see myself.

I have the right to . . . .

This is me upside down.

18

My everyday look

I AM
POWERFUL!

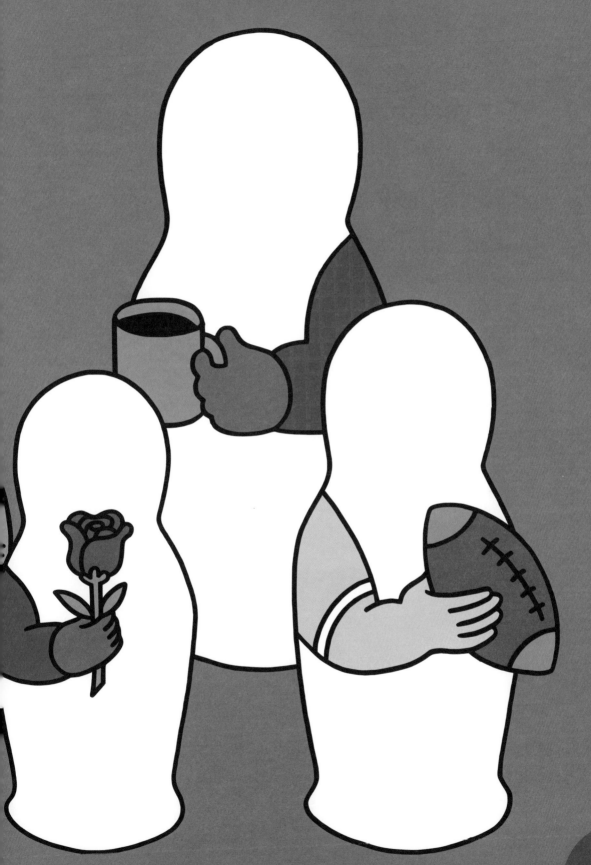

Here's what my family
thinks of me . . .

This is how I sit.

This is how I sleep.

Love notes to my favorite body parts

Foods that cheer me up

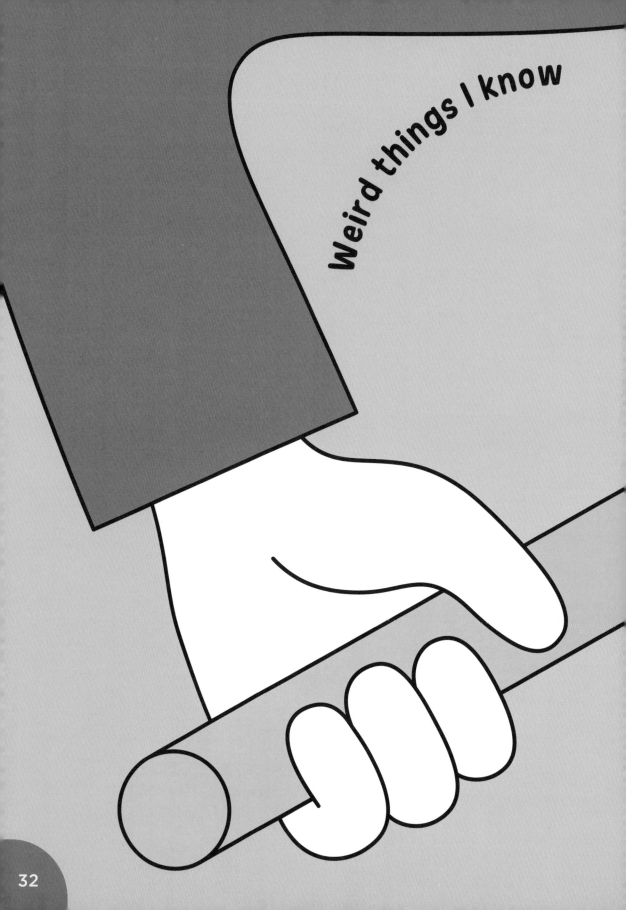

Weird things I know

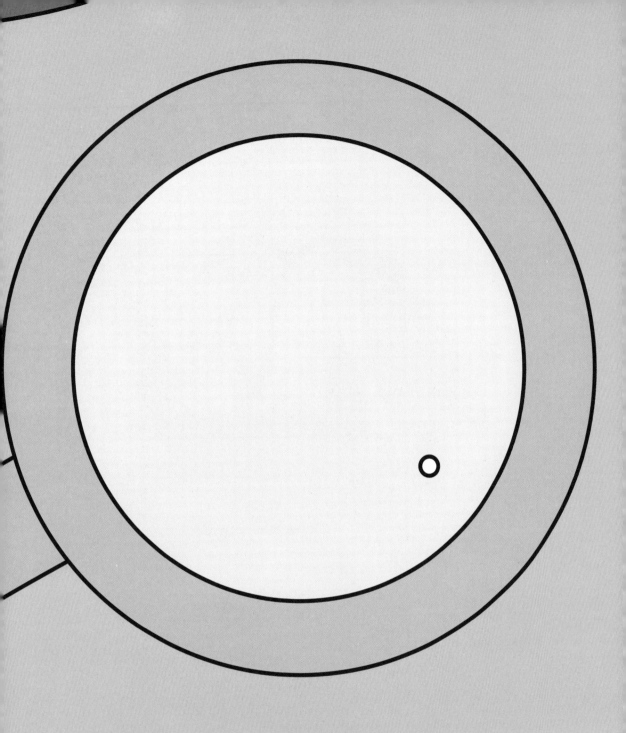

Fears I have

Fears I don't have

Things I say

to

1.

2.

3.

4.

5.

Rebel
Girls'
———
Playlist

40

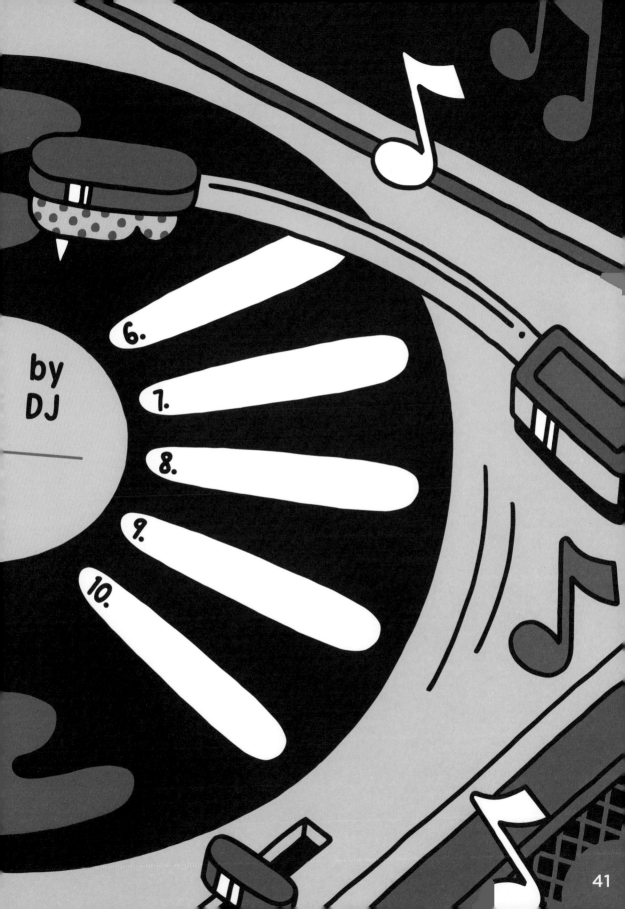

Animals
who really get me

Things I can lift!

Me belly up

My signature dance move

Things I think about
when the lights go out

Words I love

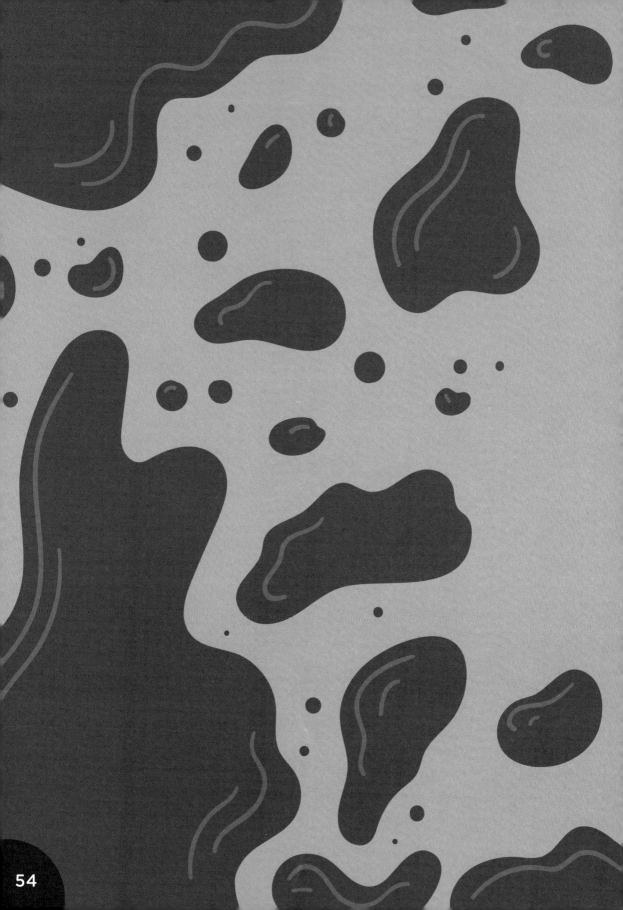

Me covered in mud

Stuff I broke

Questions I don't have answers for

My best jokes

My secret wishes

Glue these pages together to keep your secret.

Things I want IN my closet

Things
I want OUT
of my closet

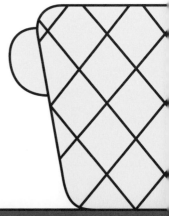

Important words I invented

People
I want
to meet

THE TINY MARTIAN

HOW DID YOU GET HERE?

Secret code

A _____   J _____   S _____

B _____   K _____   T _____

C _____   L _____   U _____

D _____   M _____   V _____

E _____   N _____   W _____

F _____   O _____   X _____

G _____   P _____   Y _____

H _____   Q _____   Z _____

I _____   R _____

Secret message

_____

_____

_____

_____

_____

_____

_____

_____

_____

_____

Secret code

A _____	H _____	O _____	V _____
B _____	I _____	P _____	W _____
C _____	J _____	Q _____	X _____
D _____	K _____	R _____	Y _____
E _____	L _____	S _____	Z _____
F _____	M _____	T _____	
G _____	N _____	U _____	

IT'S OK TO BE AFRAID.

Stuff that
makes me angry

Villains I'm going to defeat

Things worth fighting for

INTERVIEW WITH
THE BRAVEST WOMAN I KNOW

....

_____
_____
_____
_____

_____
_____
_____
_____
_____
_____
_____

_____
_____
_____
_____
_____

THE PIRATE QUEEN

These rules don't make sense to me.

My march

Dear future me,

Me as a GIANT

An incredible invention

Things my friends are good at

101

My business

103

Ways to make $10

Ways to save $10

Something weird happened to me . . .

Books I'm going
to write

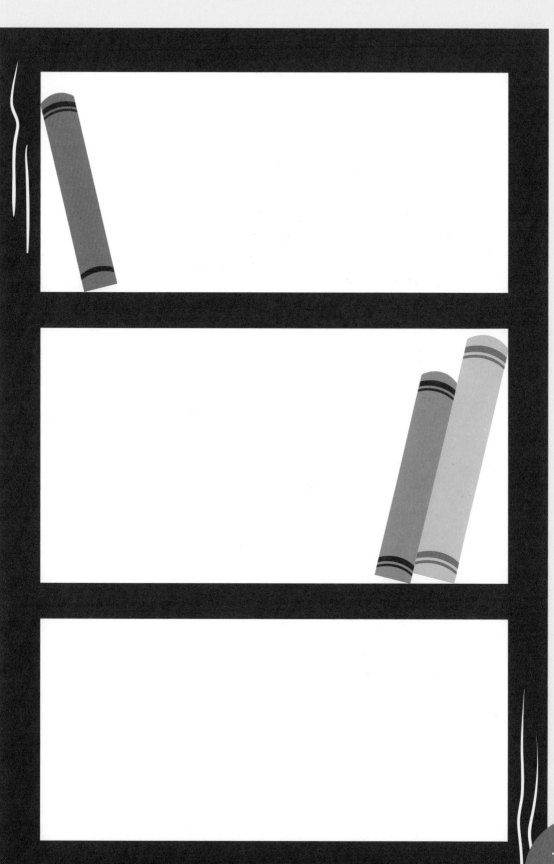

Me as a fairy

My career plan

Age 18

Age 90

Age 60

Age 40

Age 25

115

Dear _____ ,

I need help with . . .

_____

_____

_____

_____

_____

_____

_____

_____

_____

_____

_____

_____

_____

Would you help me?

☐   ☐   ☐

Yes   No   _____

I'M THE
RIGHT PERSON
AT THE RIGHT TIME
IN THE RIGHT
PLACE.

My biggest dream

122

This award
goes to . . . ME!

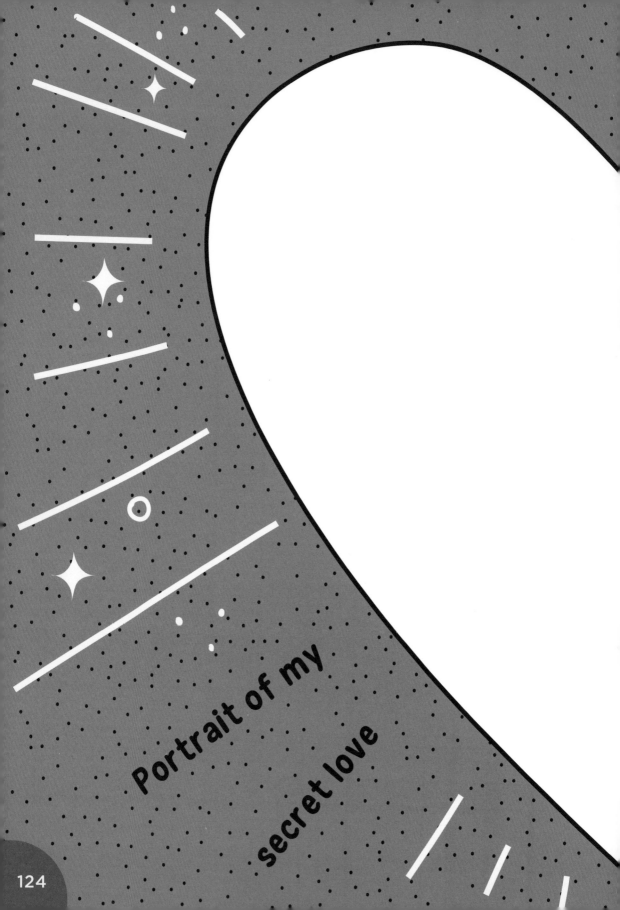

Portrait of my

secret love

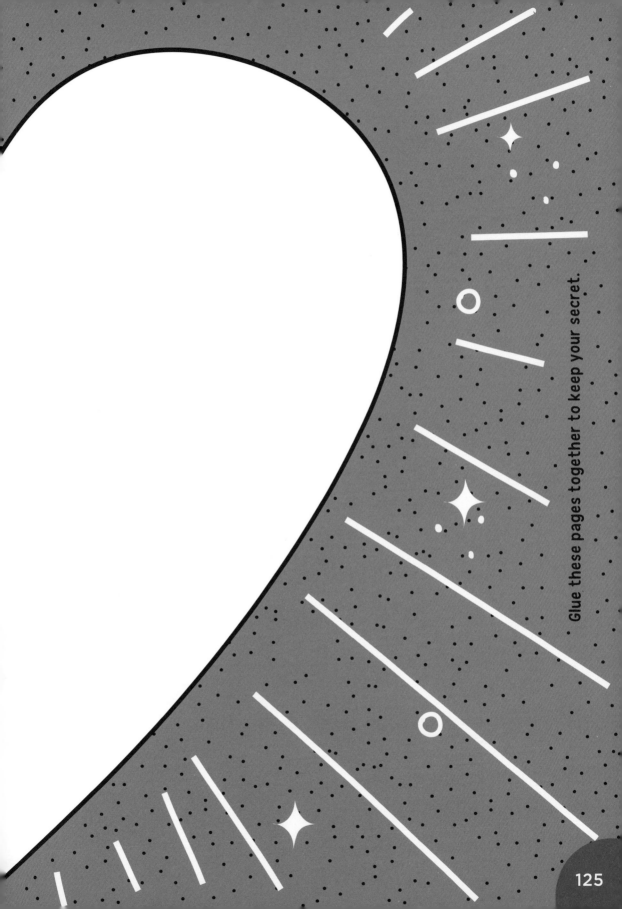

Glue these pages together to keep your secret.

WILL YOU GO OUT WITH ME?

When:

_____

Where:

_____

☐ | ☐ | ☐

Oh, yes!   Not sure   No!

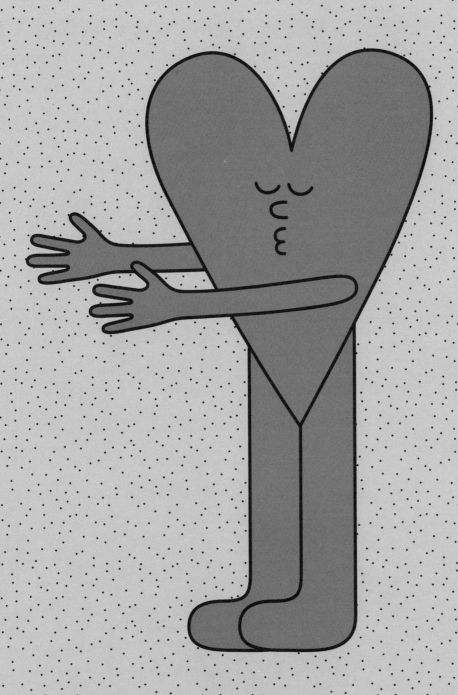

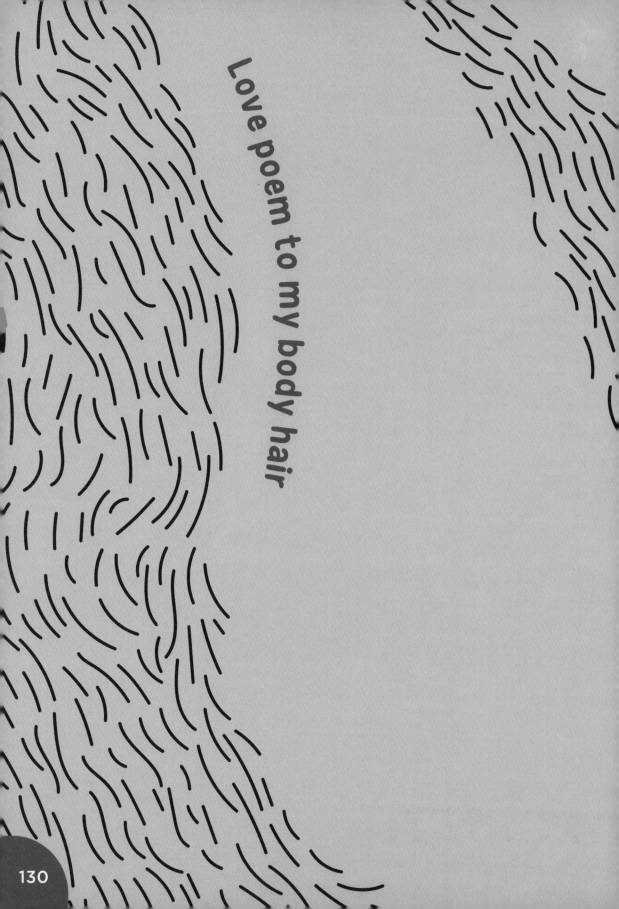

Love poem to my body hair

131

Feelings I hide behind

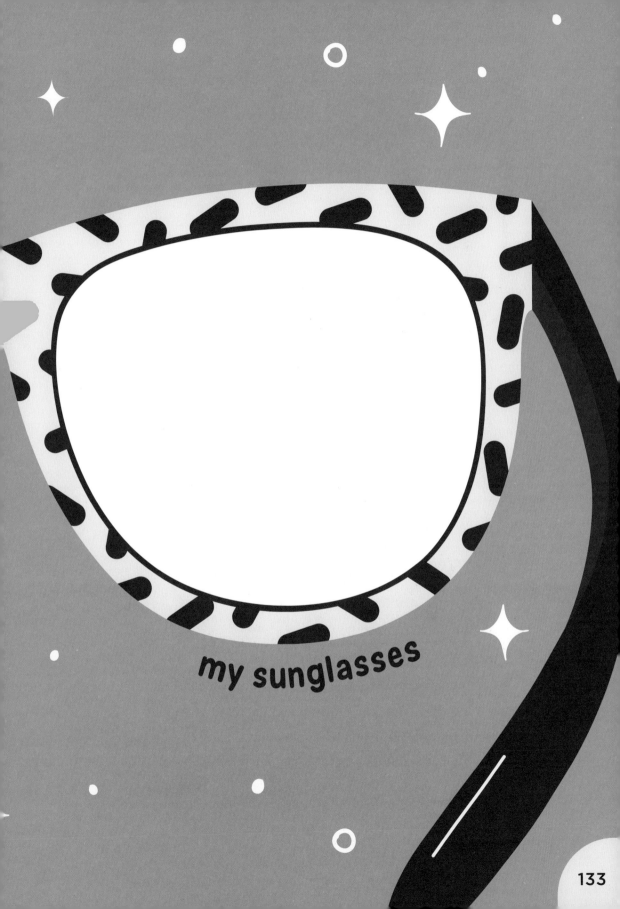

my sunglasses

Rebel Girls' Fort

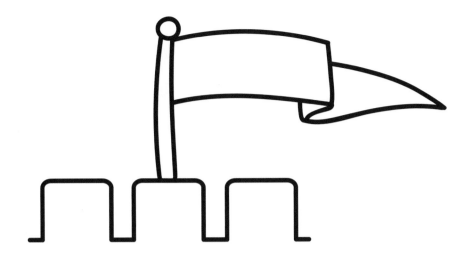

Rebel girls
I'm proud of

Rebel Girls' Rap ♥

A serenade to my love

Important words in
other languages

Plan for a day of adventure

Me on a mountain

Books to bring on a desert island

Dear _____,

I miss you . . .

_____
_____
_____
_____
_____
_____
_____
_____
_____
_____
_____
_____
_____
_____
_____
_____
_____
_____

I'M
WORTH
IT!

Questions
I haven't been asked

BEFORE

AFTER

MADAM PRESIDENT

My currency

20

40

50

20

Things I'm thirsty for

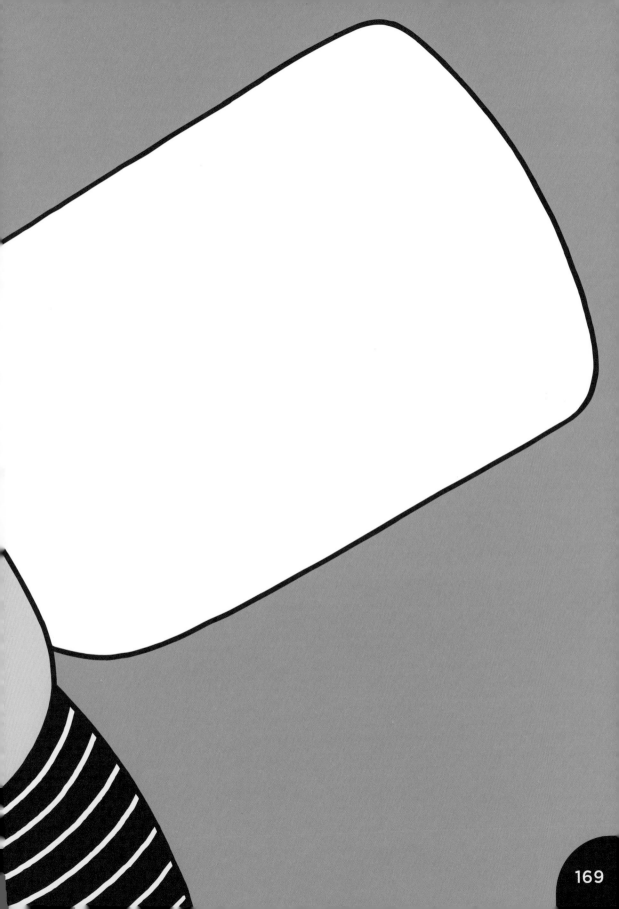

CUP _____

CUP _____

CUP _____

CUP _____

SPOON _____

SPOON _____

Recipe for disaster

The Sadness Corner

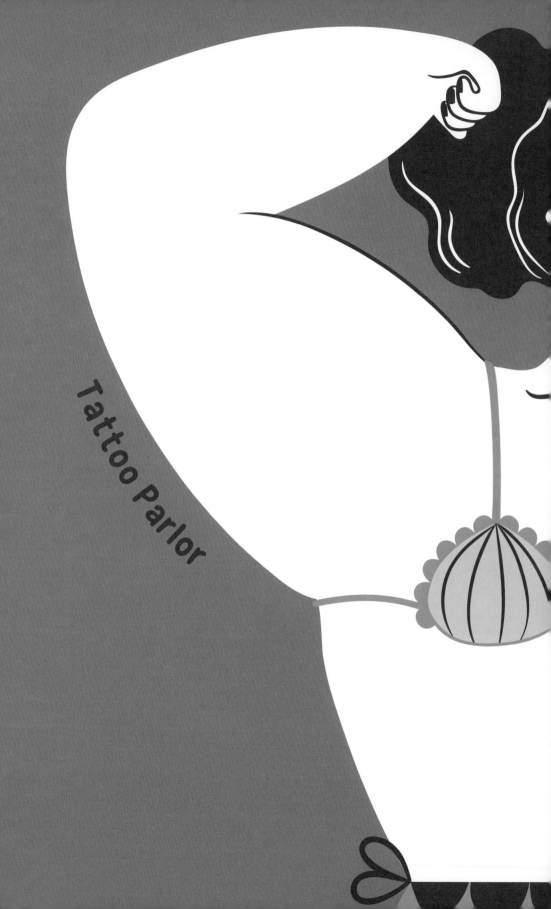

Tattoo Parlor

Letter to
an elected
representative

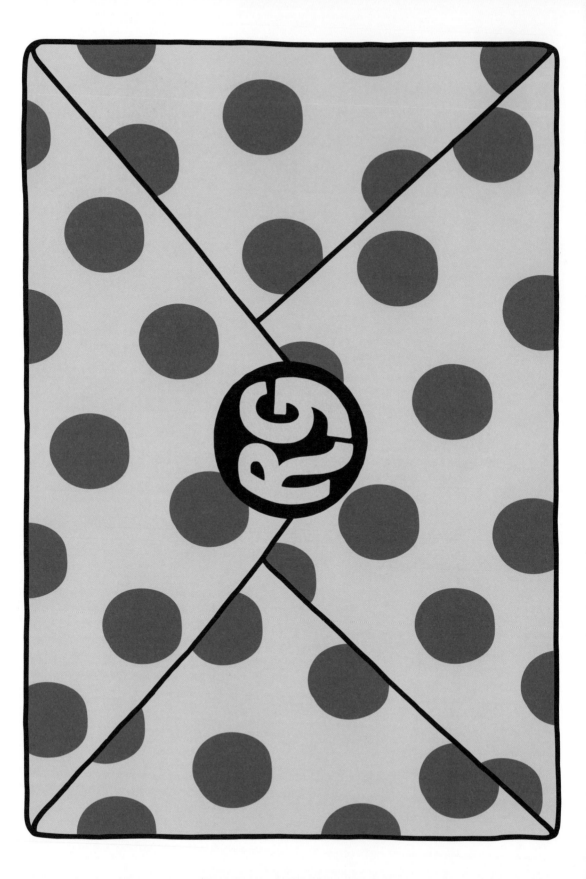

THE
REVOLUTION
STARTS
WITH ME!

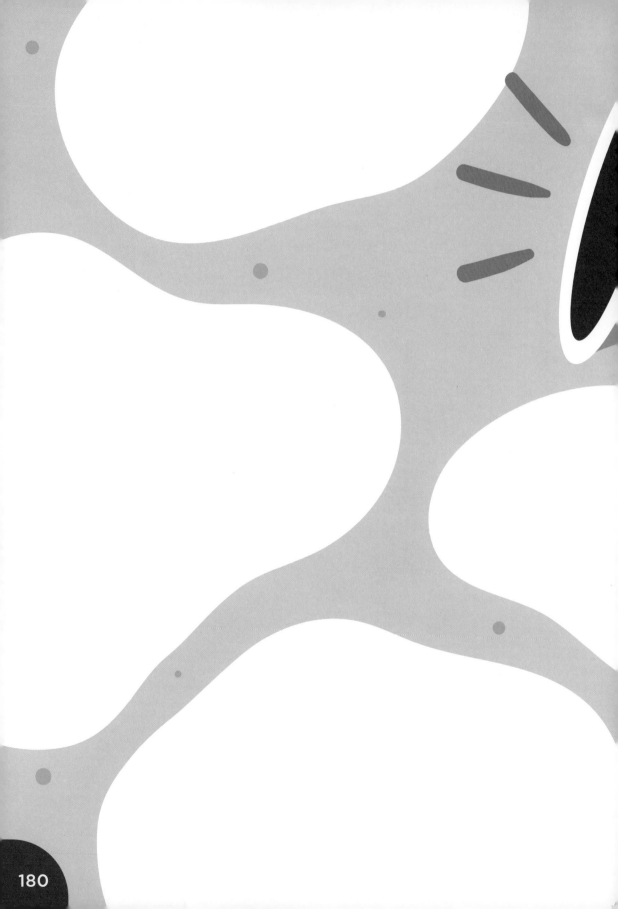

Mind-blowing ideas

Me underwater

What my friends
think of me . . .

Sell this page!

I sold this
page for

Things to let go

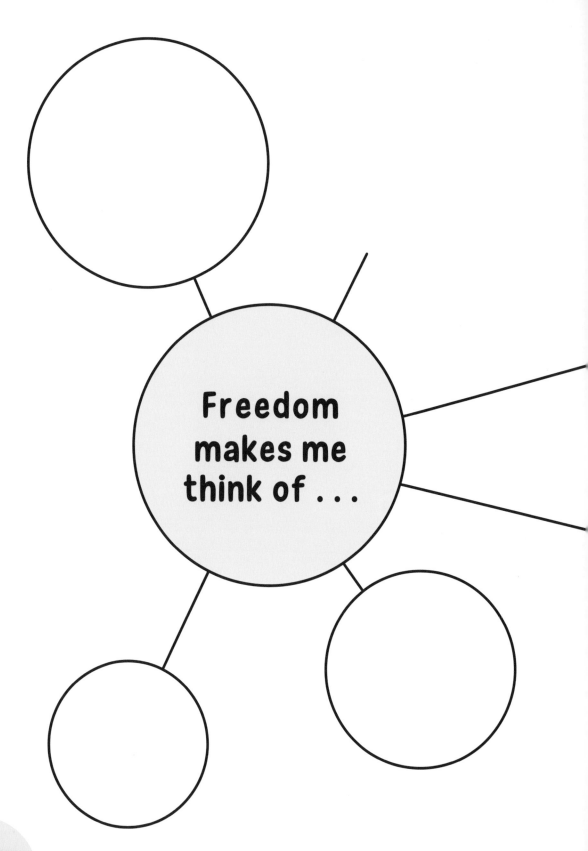

Freedom makes me think of . . .

All the feelings

I've felt today

Me riding a unicorn really fast

My flag

Battle Plan

We're stronger together.

Strategy Meeting

Protest

Dance Party

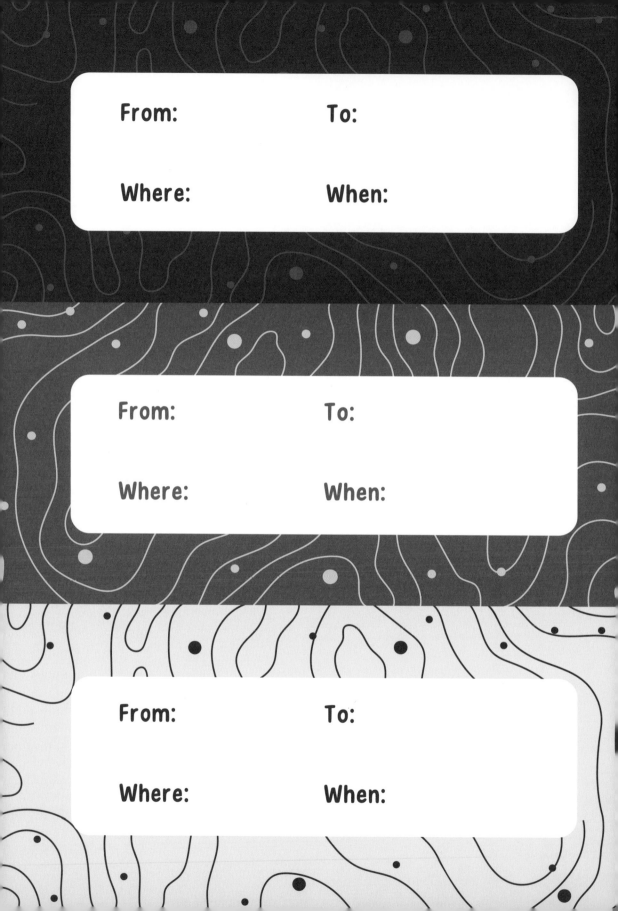

From:

To:

Where:

When:

From:

To:

Where:

When:

From:

To:

Where:

When:

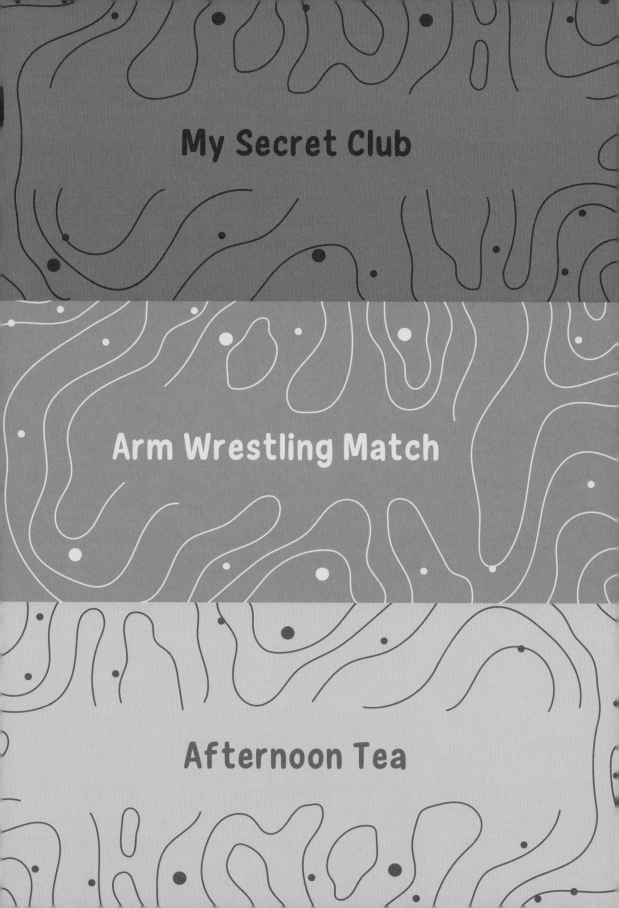

My Secret Club

Arm Wrestling Match

Afternoon Tea

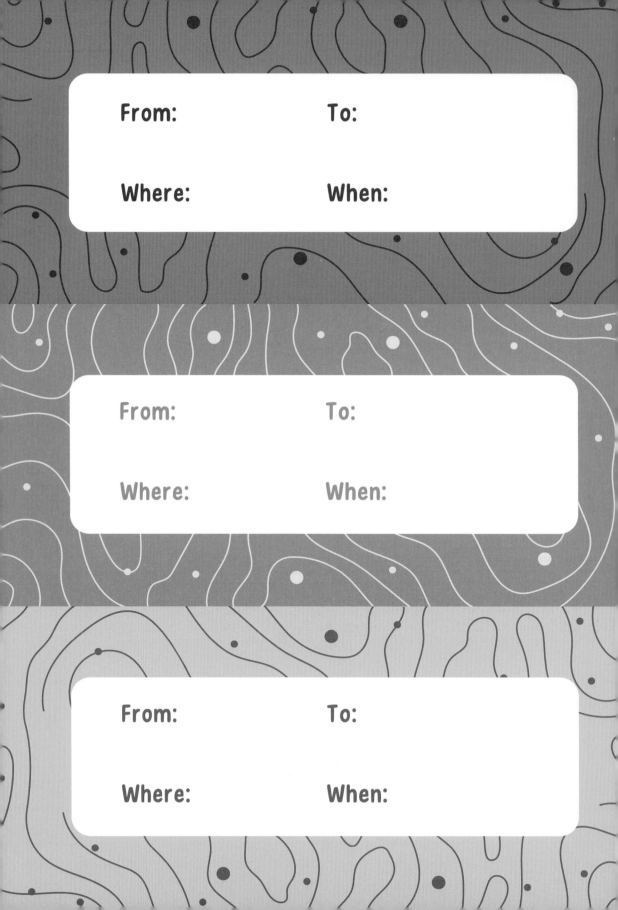

From:

To:

Where:

When:

From:

To:

Where:

When:

From:

To:

Where:

When:

SPEAK.
THE WORLD
IS LISTENING.

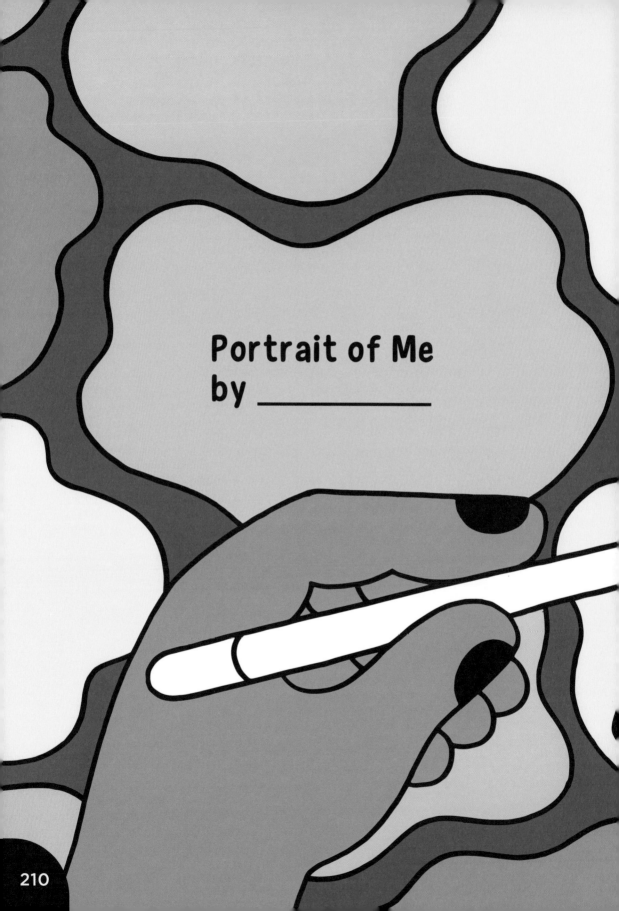

Portrait of Me
by _____

What my future holds

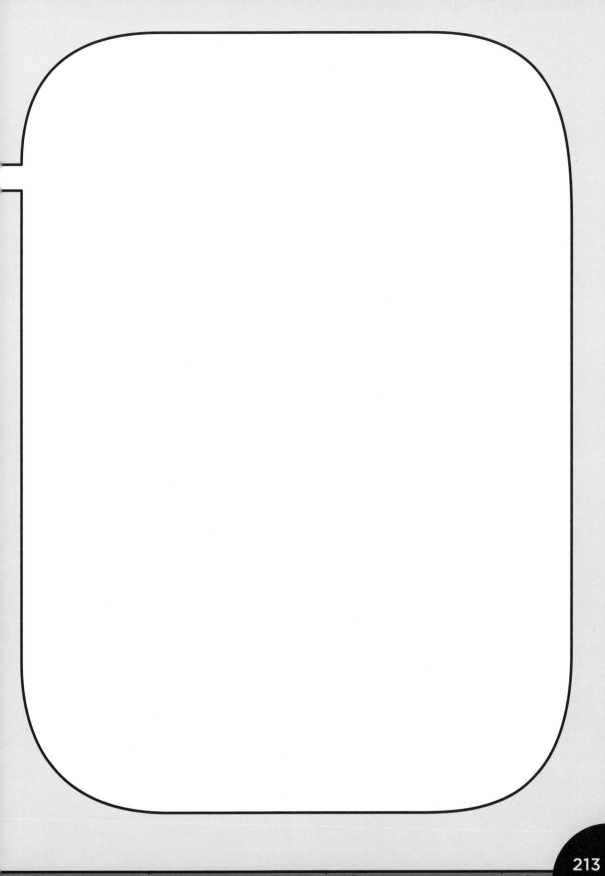

Please stop giving me . . .

Thank you ALL!!!

One more thing . . .

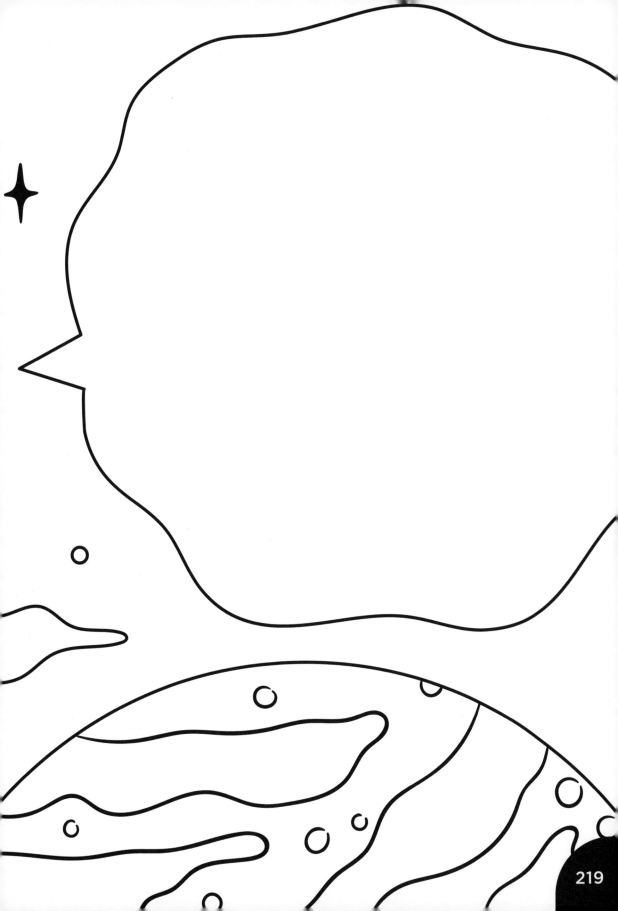

KEEP READING WITH REBEL GIRLS

www.rebelgirls.com

GOOD NIGHT STORIES FOR REBEL GIRLS IS ALSO A BEAUTIFUL PODCAST!

Listen to the stories of incredible women read by some of the most influential voices of our time.

Go to **www.rebelgirls.com/podcast** or find it wherever you get your podcasts!

REVOLUTIONS
ARE FOR SHARING!

Join the Rebel Girls' community and share your
creations with fellow rebels around the world

Facebook: www.facebook.com/rebelgirls
Instagram: @rebelgirls
Twitter: @rebelgirls

Use the hashtags #IAMAREBELGIRL and #REBELGIRLSJOURNAL
in your posts and tell us about your journey as a rebel girl
on the Facebook group The Rebel Girls Movement:
facebook.com/groups/therebelmovement

We'll see you there!

⭐ Acknowledgments ⭐

Our heartfelt thank you goes to our unbelievable community of rebels, who once again supported our Kickstarter campaign with incredible enthusiasm and generosity. There is no better feeling than knowing we are not alone and that so many people out there are fighting for freedom and equality, each in their own way.

To our team, thank you for inspiring us every day. Thank you for your hard work, for your irony, for taking care of one another, and for never stepping back from a challenge. We could not be prouder of the company we're building together.

About the Authors

Elena Favilli is a *New York Times* bestselling author and the founder of Rebel Girls. She lives in Los Angeles with her dog Lafayette, a Bracco Italiano.

Francesca Cavallo is an award-winning writer and theater director. She lives in Los Angeles.

Rebel Girls is an award-winning cultural media engine founded in 2012, spanning over 70 countries. Rebel Girls is on a mission to empower a generation of inspired and confident girls through diverse stories that resonate with audiences of all ages, celebrating women's accomplishments and pursuits throughout history, around the world, and in various fields. This diverse and passionate group of rebels works in Los Angeles, New York, Atlanta, Merida, London, and Milan.

For occasional updates on our new projects, subscribe at:
www.rebelgirls.com/signup

If you liked this book, please take a minute to review it!

Draw yourself climbing a mountain,
write love notes to your favorite body parts,
plan your revolution. The perfect companion to
the book series Good Night Stories for Rebel Girls,
I Am a Rebel Girl is an illustrated journal filled with
100 activities designed to help girls
train their rebel spirit.

—

ELENA FAVILLI is a *New York Times* bestselling author and the
founder of Rebel Girls. She lives in Los Angeles with her dog
Lafayette, a Bracco Italiano.

FRANCESCA CAVALLO is an award-winning writer and theater director.
She lives in Los Angeles.

Timbuktu Labs, Inc.
520 Broadway Suite 200 Santa Monica, CA 90401
Printed in Guangdong, China
June 2020

ISBN: 978-1-7348770-3-8
Not for individual resale